BOOK 6

Learn to Read with
Janet and John

When things go wrong!

Published by
Star Kids Ltd.,
10 Greycoat Place,
London SW1P 1SB

Authors: Penny Coltman, Jayne Greenwood and Val Mitchell

Illustrations: Colin Bowler
Liz Pichon (pages 10,11,12, 20, 21, 22).

Prepared by Tandem Design, Southampton.

First published 2001

© Star Kids 2001

A CIP record for this book is available from the British Library.

ISBN 1 84258 0590

Printed in Spain

Wash Day

"Put your dirty clothes in the
basket please," said Mum.
"We are doing the washing today."

Janet and John take the basket to Mum.
"Thank you," said Mum.
"Now you can help me to put the washing
4   into the machine."

Mum puts the powder into the machine
and turns it on.

Tim looks at the washing going round.

His red blanket will be as good as new.

When mum takes the washing out of the machine she gets a surprise.

"Oh Tim! What have you done?"

Accident words

wobble   slip   trip

slide

fall

stuck

drop

bump   spill

Keeping safe

fireguard

stairgate

cycle helmet

pads on elbows and knees

car seat

seatbelt

The Puncture

Janet and John went for a bike ride.
Mum and Tim went with them.
They went to the park.

John's bike began to wobble.
Mum said, "You have a flat tyre.
We must stop. We will call Dad."

Mum called Dad.
"Come and get us at once. John has
a flat tyre. Bring the car."
"I will come now," said Dad.

Dad put the bikes in the boot.
They all got in the car to go home.
Dad said, "I am sorry about
your bike, John, but I will fix it."

The car began to wobble.
John said, "You have a flat tyre.
We must stop."
"I will fix it," said Dad.

Dad pulled all the bikes out of the car.
It is getting dark.

Janet, John and Tim are asleep.
Mum is phoning the garage.

Tools

hammer

spanner

nails

screwdriver

screws

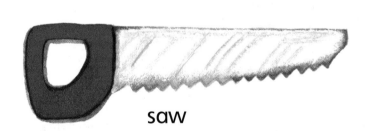

saw

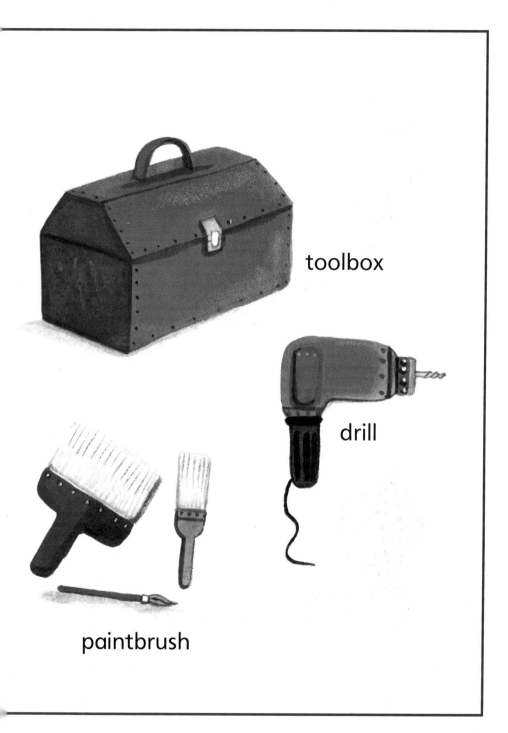

toolbox

drill

paintbrush

mechanic

decorator

plumber

gardener

carpenter

Mum's New Shelf

Mum needs a place for her cookbooks.
Dad is going to put up a
new shelf for the books.

Dad takes Janet and John to
the shop to get some wood.
"We will need some screws
as well," said Dad.

"Do you need some help?"
said the shop keeper.
"No, thank you, I know what to do,"
said Dad.

"I would like to have the shelf
by the window," said Mum.
"OK," said Dad, "it will not take long."
Janet and John helped Dad
to put the shelf up.

"At last," said Mum.
"I will put my books on the shelf now."
Janet and John were tired.
They all went to bed.

In the night there was a big crash!
"Is that Tim?" asked Dad.
28   "Let us all go and see," said Mum.

"I can fix it," said Dad.
"It won't take long!"

Key Word Reading

Below are listed the Key Words contained in this book.

Key Words are those that make up most of the
English language.

It is important that your child knows these words.
They are often repeated for emphasis, and used with
other phonic words - that is, words which can be
sounded out by children.

a	in
of	to
and	is
was	he
it	the
with	

had	some
are	has
there	at
have	out
they	her
for	his
see	we
go	she
not	be
will	all
three	make

on	big
very	made
so	because

other	came
an	over
look	new
too	him
but	were
said	

Janet and John™

Helping your child learn to read

Here is the solution for all parents who want to help their children become confident readers. Janet and John are back for today's kids, with enjoyable new stories and characters they love.

Your child's complete introduction to reading

- 8 clearly structured books progressively build your child's vocabulary
- Comprehensive coverage of the 100 key words required for 70% of language learning – a complete course
- Written and reviewed by teachers, educationalists and parents
- Supports what your kids do at school

£2.50

Star Kids

For more great fun learning, advice and activities, visit
www.JanetandJohn.com

ISBN 1-8425-8059-0

9 781842 580592